# Happy

A Cherrytree Book

Designed and produced by
A S Publishing

First published 1993
by Cherrytree Press Ltd
Windsor Bridge Road
Bath, Avon BA2 3AX

Reprinted 1995

Copyright © Cherrytree Press Ltd 1993

British Library Cataloguing in Publication Data
Amos, Janine
  Happy. – (Feelings Series)
  I. Title  II. Green, Gwen  III. Series
  152.4

ISBN 0-7451-5197-3

Printed and bound in Spain by Graficas Reunidas, S.A.

# Happy

By Janine Amos
Illustrated by Gwen Green

CHERRYTREE BOOKS

# Zoë's story

Zoë had brought her friends home after school.

"We'll have tea first, then we can go to the park," said Zoë. "Come on!" She dashed into the kitchen.

"Shh!" said Zoë's mum. She looked worried. "Your gran's had a fall. She needs some peace."

Everyone was quiet. They all liked Zoë's gran.

"Where is she?" asked Zoë.

Zoë's mum didn't get a chance to answer. There was a shout from the front room.

"I'm in here. Come in and see me!" called Gran.

All four girls ran into the front room.

Gran was sitting in her chair. She had lots of cushions behind her.

"Hello, girls," said Gran. "I slipped over in the bath!"

"Does it hurt?" asked Sophie.

"Not much," said Gran, "but the doctor told me to rest my leg. I have to stay home for three whole weeks."

"But what about your birthday treat?" said Zoë.

"Zoë's mum was taking me to see a show," Gran told the others. "Now I can't go. Silly old leg."

Gran laughed but she didn't look happy.

"Poor Gran," said Zoë, giving her a kiss.

**How do you think Zoë's gran feels?**

Later, in the park, the girls talked about Zoë's gran.

"She was nearly crying because she can't go to that show," said Zoë.

"We should put on our own show," said Sophie. "Especially for your gran."

"What sort of show?" asked Louise.

"Something with singing, and dancing – and some jokes," said Sophie.

"A Birthday Show!" said Zoë. "That's a brilliant idea!"

Every day at lunchtime and after school the girls practised hard. Jo and Louise borrowed a tape. They worked out a dance together. Sophie's big brother lent her his box of tricks. Louise had a joke book. The girls learnt two jokes and two tricks each. They made costumes from old clothes. They made each other laugh.

"Let's end with a song," said Sophie.
"Which song?" asked Louise.
"That's easy!" shouted the others.
They were all looking forward to Saturday.
"It's fun planning a show," said Jo.
"I bet Gran will be pleased," thought Zoë.

**Can you guess what the song will be?**

On Gran's birthday the girls gave her an invitation.
They all crowded round while Gran read the words:
You are invited to
GRAN'S BIRTHDAY SHOW
at 16.30 today
FREE

Gran gave them a big smile. "I'll wear my best dress," she said.

That afternoon the girls were very excited. They waited while Gran sat down. Zoë's mum was there too – and Badger the dog. Then Zoë turned off the lights. Sophie put on the tape. The show began.

Everything went well and all the tricks worked. The girls made everyone laugh.

At the very end, Sophie, Zoë, Jo and Louise joined hands. They sang "Happy Birthday to You". Badger howled.

Gran and Zoë's mum clapped for a long time.

"Bravo!" called Gran.

**How do you think the girls feel? How does Gran feel now?**

Afterwards they were all invited to Gran's birthday tea.

"Thank you, everyone," said Gran. "That was a great show. I really am having a happy birthday."

"So am I," said Zoë, "and it isn't even my birthday!"

Sophie, Louise and Jo knew just what she meant.

## Feeling like Zoë

Zoë and her friends set out to cheer up Zoë's gran. They ended by having a good time themselves, too. Has this ever happened to you?

## Happy with friends

Doing something with a group of friends can be a lot of fun. Everyone has his or her special part. When all the parts are put together, you'll have made a whole project.

## Helping others

Lots of people are happy doing things together in a team or club. And, as Zoë found, planning and practising are all part of the fun. What things do you do with your friends which make you happy? What could you do to help make another person happy?

## Think about it

You can be happy in lots of different ways. Read the stories in this book. Think about the people in the stories. Do you feel like them sometimes? What kinds of things make you feel happy?

# Sarah's story

It was the last day of the summer holidays. Sarah's family was busy – far too busy to bother about Sarah.

"Don't talk to me now, Sarah," said her big brother Richard. "I have to get this project finished."

"Stop getting under my feet, Sarah," said her mum. "It's school tomorrow and I have a lot to get ready."

"I want to go somewhere," Sarah moaned. "I don't want to be on my own."

"Maybe later," said Sarah's mum. "Why don't you do some writing? Write about the holiday."

Sarah pulled a face. "We'll do that at school tomorrow, in any case," she said.

"Scram!" said Sarah's mum, laughing.

Sarah went to her room and looked out at the rain. She watched a raindrop run down the window. She followed it with her finger. And she thought about her summer holiday.

Sarah's family had been on a touring holiday. Sarah had collected a postcard from every place.

**How do you think Sarah feels?**

Sarah sat down and looked at the postcards one by one. She wondered what else she had collected. She shook her duffle bag on to the bed. Out rolled two foreign coins and a sea shell. Then Sarah searched through her jacket pockets. She found lots of entrance tickets – to caves and castles. She found a feather and an old sweet wrapper.

There was soon a pile of things on Sarah's bed. She looked at them all carefully. Sarah could hear Richard coughing in the next room. She could hear her mum talking on the 'phone. Sarah started to hum.

Sarah got out some big sheets of paper, some felt pens and some glue. She started with the postcard of the caves. She glued it on to the paper. Next to the postcard she wrote:

"We visited these caves. They were cold and dark."

She glued the entrance ticket near to the picture.

Underneath she drew round the French coin.

"It cost this much to get in," she wrote.

Sarah filled up pages and pages with her collection.

**Do you think Sarah feels happy now?**

When Sarah's mum came in, Sarah was busy.

"That looks interesting," said Sarah's mum.

"It's a book about our holiday," Sarah explained.

"I'm ready to take you somewhere now," said Sarah's mum. "Don't you want to see some friends?"

But Sarah had changed her mind.

"I'll see them tomorrow at school," she said, smiling. "Today I like being on my own."

**Why do you think Sarah changed her mind?**

## Feeling like Sarah

At first, Sarah wasn't happy with her own company. She wanted to be with her friends. But everyone has to be on their own sometimes. And part of growing up is learning to enjoy being alone. It's a different sort of happiness from being with friends. It's a quiet sort of happiness.

## Happy on your own

Sarah felt happy remembering her holiday. She enjoyed putting her collection into a book. What do you like doing when you're by yourself? Are you reading this book on your own? Are you feeling happy now?

# Greg's story

Greg's mum was sitting on the kitchen floor. There were heaps of clothes around her. There were pots, pans, a torch and some long poles. Greg thought he could see a tent.

"Hurry up with your breakfast," said his mum. "We're going camping!" Greg's mum was always full of surprises.

Greg's sister Gemma came in. She looked at all the mess. "We never go camping," said Gemma, yawning.

"Well, we are now," said their mum. "Your dad's not very happy. We'll cheer him up. We'll take him camping!"

"But Dad hates camping!" said Greg.

"He'll love it!" said Greg's mum.

It took nearly all morning to load the car.

"Off we go!" called Greg's mum at last. She got into the driving seat.

"It looks like rain," said Greg's dad.

But Greg didn't think his mum was listening. She was giving everyone jobs.

"Greg and I will pitch the tent," she said. "Gemma, you can sort out lunch with your dad."

Greg thought his dad looked fed up.

At the campsite Greg and his mum got out the tent. It took them ages to put it up. It wouldn't stand straight. When they had finished, they sat down on the grass, puffing. The tent leaned over to one side. Greg couldn't help laughing.

"It's a bit wobbly," said Greg's mum, "but it will do."

Greg's dad and Gemma were trying to cook baked beans. They had a little camping stove. Every time the wind blew, the stove went out.

"I'm giving up!" said Greg's dad at last. "Let's eat them cold."

Greg and Gemma shared a can of cold baked beans. Greg thought they tasted great.

After lunch they walked to the beach. Greg and Gemma went for a swim. Later they all made a giant sandcastle.

"Stand behind it and I'll take a photograph," called Greg's mum.

Just then a huge wave crashed on to the beach. It washed right over the sandcastle.

"Storm's coming," said Greg's dad. "Time to go."

"Oh, no. The tent!" thought Greg.

They ran as fast as they could back to the campsite. It was raining hard. The ground was sticky with mud. The tent had flopped down on to the grass. It was full of water. All the sleeping bags were wet through.

"Everything's going wrong!" worried Greg. "This won't make Dad happy."

"Let's pack up the tent and sit in the car!" shouted Greg's dad.

**How do you think Greg feels?**

Soon the tent was packed away. Greg's mum gave everyone a towel and they rubbed themselves dry. Greg's dad got out a flask of hot chocolate. They sipped the chocolate and looked out at the mud.

"I hate camping," said Greg's dad.

Then Greg's dad started to laugh. Greg's mum looked at him and grinned. She began laughing too. Gemma joined in.

Greg looked round at his family.

"Everything's gone wrong," he said, giggling. "But it doesn't matter at all!"

**How do Greg and his family feel now?**

## Feeling like Greg

Greg was worried that his dad wouldn't like camping. He was worried that the rain might spoil the trip. And he was surprised when his dad ended up in a good mood. Have you ever felt like Greg?

## The unexpected

Happiness is often unexpected. Lots of things may go wrong, but you can still have a good time. The people you are with can help you.

## Happiness happens

You can't make yourself feel happy. It just happens! But it's easy to be happy when you're with a group of people who care about you. Who makes you feel happy? Can you think of the people you help to make happy?

## Feeling happy

Happiness is a good feeling. You don't have to have expensive toys or lots of money to be happy. As Zoë, Sarah and Greg found out, you can be happy doing ordinary things. Think about the stories in this book. What was the last thing that gave you happiness? What are you going to do tomorrow that will make you feel happy?

If you are feeling frightened or unhappy, don't keep it to yourself. Talk to an adult you can trust, like a parent or a teacher. If you feel really alone, you could telephone or write to one of these offices. Remember, there is always someone who can help.

## Childline
Freephone 0800 1111
Address: Freepost 1111, London N1 0BR

## Childline for children in care
Freephone 0800 884444 (6 – 10pm)

## NSPCC Child Protection Line
Freephone 0800 800500

## The Samaritans
Dial 100 – The operator will put you through.